Dream Big!
Using Your Imagination

Sally Huss
with
Elizabeth Hamilton-Guarino

"Goodnight. Goodnight.

Wishing you sweet dreams tonight,"

Said my mother in a voice so soft and kind.

And that is exactly what I had in mind.

Whether it's day or night, I like to use my imagination.

And tonight was just such an occasion.

So, I let my imagination take flight.

And, off I went on a magic carpet of light.

This sent me to the most unusual land

Where everyone there lends a helping hand.

I could see, for instance, to plant a flower in a pot

May take more hands than one has got.

Or, it could be that someone needs help

buttoning a shirt or zipping a zipper…

Or putting on a furry slipper.

Other hands can help get things done.

Besides that, sharing tasks can be fun.

That was just the beginning. Next, I decided to fly

to the land of smiling faces,

Where smiles are found all over the places.

As I discovered, a smile makes the perfect mirror

To make another smile appear.

Big ones, small ones, round ones, tall ones –

only smiles as far as I could see.

That happy sight, I confess, put a smile on me.

Now, where else could my imagination soar?

Perhaps someplace I'd never been before.

Ah yes… to the land of gladly giving.

This is a place where everyone is happy to be living.

Gifts of food, gifts of flowers, gifts of books…

Gifts of toys, and poems, and gifts of kind looks.

Everyone is giving to others,

All seem to act like sisters and brothers.

Each gives to another and another gives to her or him.

This seems to go on and on without end.

Off I go again, this time to the land of big dreams I fly,

Where the possibilities of greatness are revealed in this sky.

There were even dreams of greatness of something I could be.

Is it possible that I could be whatever I'd like to be?

Why not?

It might be a teacher, an author, a sportsman, an actor…

A singer, a painter, a musician, a doctor…

A chef, a soldier, or even the President,

Or, something else I might invent.

Whatever I decide, I promised myself that I'd do the best I can

And with planning and effort I could become a very great man.

From there I chose to direct my flight

To the most important land that night –

The land of thanksgiving,

Where I learned that being grateful was the best way of living

All I could hear was, "Thank you for this day.

Thank you for this night.

Thank you for my friends and family,

those close and those out of sight.

Thank you for all of life that loves me

and makes me feel at home

And reminds that I am never ever alone."

These words float into the sky

As I hang onto my carpet while I fly by.

But now it's time to get some sleep.

I slip back under my covers without making a peep…

And remember the lands that I visited and what I learned:

To be helpful and happy and do others a good turn,

To enjoy each day and give what I can

And be thankful for all that I have and all that I am.

Dreaming big sets in motion all the good things

that I could want and be and do.

You too can dream big. It's all up to you.

The end,
but not the end
of dreaming big.

At the end of this book, you will find a Certificate of Merit that may be issued to any child who has fulfilled the requirements stated in the certificate. This fine certificate will easily fit into a 5"x7" frame, and happily suit any girl or boy who receives it.

Here are more books by Sally Huss and Elizabeth Hamilton-Guarino that you might enjoy. They may be found on Amazon along with the rest of Sally's extensive collection of children's books designed to delight and inspire!

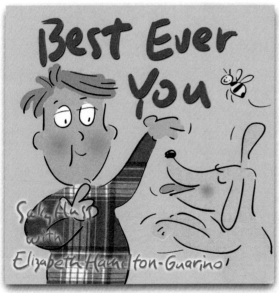

About the Contributors

Sally Huss

Author/illustrator Sally Huss creates children's books to uplift the lives of children. She does this by giving them tools to overcome obstacles; by helping them value themselves and others; and by inspiring them to be the best that they can be. Her catalog of books now exceeds 100.

"Bright and happy," "light and whimsical" have been the catch phrases attached to the writings and art of Sally Huss for over 30 years. Sweet images dance across all of Sally's creations, whether in the form of children's books, paintings, wallpaper, ceramics, baby bibs, purses, clothing, or her King Features syndicated newspaper panel *Happy Musings*.

Formerly, Sally was a tennis champion (#1 US Junior player, Wimbledon semi-finalist.) She created a Zen approach to the game and taught her method on courts and clubs from Aspen to Beverly Hills and Malibu. Presently, she teaches at the renown Garden of the Gods Resort in Colorado Springs.

Sally is a graduate of USC with a degree in Fine Art and through the years has had 6 of her own licensed art galleries throughout the world. sallyhuss.com.

Elizabeth Hamilton-Guarino

Elizabeth-Hamilton-Guarino is the founder of The Best Ever You Network and Chi Executive Officer of Compliance4. Through these companies, she has helped individua and organizations around the world be their best and achieve world-class excellence wi gratitude-based behavior and belief systems. She is one of America's foremost personal ar corporate development consultants specializing in mindset, gratitude, facilitating chang and taking action.

Guarino is the author of multiple books including her latest, *The Change Guidebook How to Align Your Heart, Truths and Energy to Find Success in All Areas of Your Life*, which was th recipient of the 2022 International Book Award for Non-Fiction.

Elizabeth lives her daily life with multiple, life-threatening food allergies. Elizabet and Sally Huss have co-authored three best-selling children's books.

Elizabeth is a member of the Forbes Business Council and serves as a leadershi advisor for the Olympia Snowe Women's Leadership Institute. She has a B.A. in journalis with honors from St. Ambrose University in Davenport, Iowa and currently attends Harvai Business School for Leadership.

Elizabeth and her husband Peter live in Maine with their four sons.

This certificate may be cut out, framed, and presented to any child who has earned it.

Certificate of Merit

_____
(Name)

The child named above is awarded this
Certificate of Merit for:
*Helping others
*Being thankful for what you have
*Dreaming big

Presented by: _____

Date: _____